KEY STAGE 2
Maths

Write your name in the space below.

Maths superstar:

How to use this book

This book will help your child to get excited about maths, if they aren't already!
It covers 12 key topics and is packed full of fun activities, colourful illustrations and jokes to boost your child's confidence and make learning fun, plus reward stickers to give them a real sense of achievement.

Getting started

Find a comfortable place to sit, away from distractions. Your child will get the most out of this book if you work through it together. Read the instructions and talk about each activity. Encourage your child by praising both their effort and their achievement.

Things to do

- Work through the pages in order, completing all the activities before moving on to the next page.
- Ask your child to place a gold star sticker at the bottom of each page once they have completed it. You might want to check the answers at the back of the book first or the page numbers will be covered by the sticker.
- You don't need to complete all the activities in one go. Try working through one or two pages every day.
- Use a pencil to write your answers. Lots of the activities can be practised again and again on a separate sheet of paper.
- You may photocopy pages for use at home.

This book covers the following topics:

- ⭐ Times tables
- ⭐ Fractions
- ⭐ Place value
- ⭐ Ordering and sequences
- ⭐ Maths operations
- ⭐ Measuring
- ⭐ 2D and 3D shapes
- ⭐ Graphs
- ⭐ Money
- ⭐ Lines of symmetry
- ⭐ Roman numerals
- ⭐ Mental maths
- ⭐ Answers

Text: Helen Jaeger, BA (Hons), PGCE
Illustrations: Amanda Gulliver
Editor: Amanda Learmonth
Design: Rebecca Wildman
Series Editor: Elizabeth Golding
Creative Director: Anton Poitier
Series educational consultants: Helen Jaeger, BA (Hons), PGCE
Amanda Learmonth BA (Hons), TESOL,
Tony Potter PhD, BEd (Hons), Cert Ed

Times tables

Times tables are essential! As well as helping you with mental maths, you need them for division, fractions, algebra and geometry. They also mean you don't have to do every sum on your fingers, because they help you "skip count." Use this grid to help you learn the times tables from 1 to 12.

Challenge!

Write or print out a 12 x 12 grid. Time yourself to see how quickly you can fill it in with your times tables. Challenge yourself regularly. Can you get faster?

	1	2	3	4	5	6	7	8	9	10	11	12
1	1	2	3	4	5	6	7	8	9	10	11	12
2	2	4	6	8	10	12	14	16	18	20	22	24
3	3	6	9	12	15	18	21	24	27	30	33	36
4	4	8	12	16	20	24	28	32	36	40	44	48
5	5	10	15	20	25	30	35	40	45	50	55	60
6	6	12	18	24	30	36	42	48	54	60	66	72
7	7	14	21	28	35	42	49	56	63	70	77	84
8	8	16	24	32	40	48	56	64	72	80	88	96
9	9	18	27	36	45	54	63	72	81	90	99	108
10	10	20	30	40	50	60	70	80	90	100	110	120
11	11	22	33	44	55	66	77	88	99	110	121	132
12	12	24	36	48	60	72	84	96	108	120	132	144

You can refer to this grid throughout the activities in this book to help you. Practise the tables you find hard, then give yourself a gold star!

Times tables: tips

Here are some tips and tricks to help you learn your times tables more quickly.

Find an anchor point
If you get stuck on a trickier times table, like 7 or 9, pick a number somewhere in the middle to check you're right so far. For example, 7 x 7 = 49. Knowing a number in the middle gives you an "anchor point."

9 times table: finding patterns
The 9 times table can be tricky to remember! Look at the chart below and fill in the missing numbers. Can you see a pattern?

1 x 9 =	0	9
2 x 9 =	1	8
3 x 9 =	2	7
4 x 9 =	3	6
5 x 9 =	4	5
6 x 9 =	5	4
7 x 9 =	6	3
8 x 9 =	7	2
9 x 9 =	8	1
10 x 9 =	9	0
11 x 9 =	9	9
12 x 9 =	10	8

Tip time!
The left column goes from 0 to 10. The right column goes from 9 to 0.

All the digits add up to 9. So 0 + 9 = 9; 1 + 8 = 9; 2 + 7 = 9 and so on.

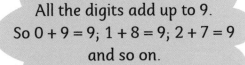

Finished? Give yourself a gold star, then it's joke time. Why do magicians make such good teachers?

Answer: They always ask trick questions!

9 times table: a handy trick

This trick is really handy! The example below shows you how to work out 2 x 9 = 18.

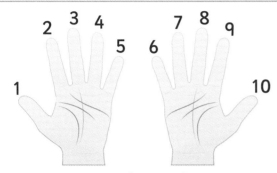

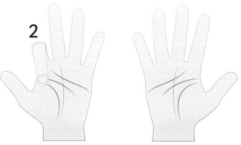

Put your hands (face up) in front of you. Each finger and thumb is numbered from 1 to 10, starting with your thumb on the left.

Put down the finger you are multiplying by. For 2 x 9, put down finger number 2.

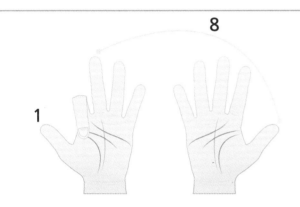

Count the fingers on either side. On the left of finger 2 is 1 thumb and on the right are 8 fingers. Put the numbers together and the answer is 18!

9 x 2 = 18

11 times table: double it up!

A quick way to remember your 11 times table is to "double up" the number you're multiplying by. For example, 2 x 11 = 22. For 11 x 10, just add a 0 = 110. Then just learn the last two: 11 x 11 = 121 and 12 x 11 = 132.

Fill in the gaps on this number wheel to complete the 11 times table.

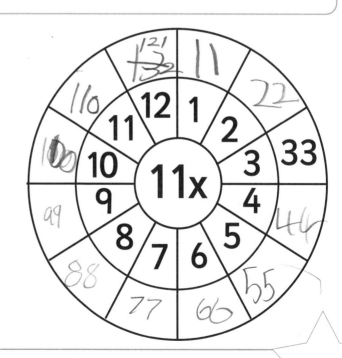

Finished? Give yourself a gold star, then it's joke time.
What did the 0 say to the 8?

Answer: Nice belt!

Fractions

If you break a bone, you have two parts (or more) instead of one.

This is called a fracture. In maths, a fraction is almost the same – it is part of a whole.

Have a go at these fraction challenges.

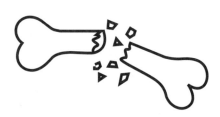

Divide it up

You're having a sleepover with three friends. Mum cooks a pizza. Fill the gaps in the sentences below.

Mum cuts the pieces of pizza into ☐ slices, so that everyone gets an equal slice (including you).

Your slice of pizza is 1 of ☐ slices.

As a fraction, that's written ☐ .

How much pizza?

How much is *one* slice of pizza as a fraction in each of these pizzas?
Write your answers below. The first one has been done for you.

$$\frac{1}{6}$$

6

Finished? Give yourself a gold star, then it's joke time.
How did the boy show the teacher that he understood fractions?

Answer: By only doing half his homework!

Whole and parts

Dad cooks another pizza. With your slice, you now have one whole pizza and one part of a pizza (one quarter). That's written as $1\frac{1}{4}$. Draw a line from each shape to the matching fraction.

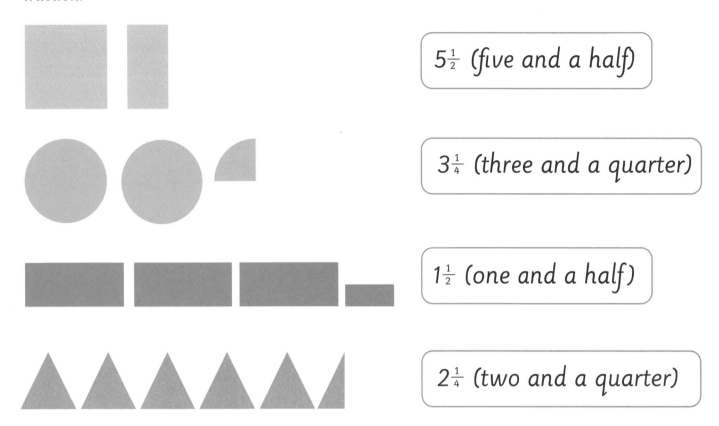

$5\frac{1}{2}$ (five and a half)

$3\frac{1}{4}$ (three and a quarter)

$1\frac{1}{2}$ (one and a half)

$2\frac{1}{4}$ (two and a quarter)

Naming fractions

Some fractions have special names, such as half, third and quarter. Write the fraction in the box next to the picture.

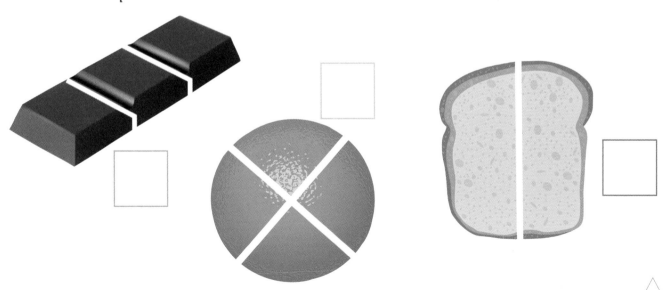

Finished? Give yourself a gold star, then it's joke time.
Who invented fractions?

Answer: King Henry the Eighth!

Fractions: adding, simplifying and subtracting

You can do sums with fractions, such as adding and subtracting. In fractions, the top number is called the numerator and the bottom number is the denominator.

$$\frac{3}{5}$$ ← numerator

← denominator

Adding fractions

It's simple to add and subtract fractions when the denominators are the same.

$$\frac{1}{4} + \frac{1}{4} = \frac{2}{4}$$

Add these fractions.

$$\frac{1}{5} + \frac{2}{5} = \frac{}{5}$$

$$\frac{2}{9} + \frac{5}{9} = \text{—}$$

$$\frac{2}{7} + \frac{3}{7} = \text{—}$$

Keep it simple

In maths, we like to simplify an answer. That means there's no more maths we can do on it! If you cut a chocolate cake into 4 slices and take 2 slices, you will have 2 slices left. You can write that as $\frac{2}{4}$.

$$\frac{4}{4}$$

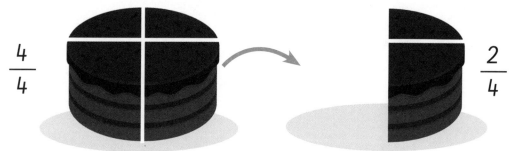

$$\frac{2}{4}$$

Both the numerator and the denominator of $\frac{2}{4}$ can be divided by 2 to give the answer $\frac{1}{2}$.

$$\frac{2 \div 2}{4 \div 2} = \frac{1}{2}$$

Simplify these fractions.

$$\frac{4}{12} = \text{—}$$

$$\frac{5}{15} = \text{—}$$

$$\frac{6}{18} = \text{—}$$

8

Finished? Give yourself a gold star, then it's joke time.
Why didn't the 4s want any dinner?

Answer: Because they already 8!

Subtracting fractions

You have $\frac{2}{4}$ (or $\frac{1}{2}$) of the chocolate cake left. You take away another $\frac{1}{4}$. Using simple subtraction, it's easy to see you'd have $\frac{1}{4}$ of the cake left:

$$\frac{2}{4}$$

$$\frac{1}{4}$$

Subtract these fractions.

$$\frac{7}{9} - \frac{5}{9} = \frac{}{9}$$

$$\frac{3}{5} - \frac{2}{5} = \frac{}{}$$

$$\frac{7}{12} - \frac{5}{12} = \frac{}{}$$

Tip time!

Remember the golden rule in maths is "like with like."

We can take away $\frac{1}{4}$ from $\frac{2}{4}$, because the denominators are the same number.

Lowest common multiple

If we want to add or subtract fractions with different denominators, we need to find the lowest common multiple.

$$\frac{1}{2} - \frac{1}{4} = \frac{}{}$$

That means the lowest number both denominators go into, with no remainders. To find the lowest common multiple of $\frac{2}{4}$, find the multiples of 2 and 4:

Multiples of 2:
2 4 6 8 10 12

Multiples of 4:
4 8 12 16 20

The lowest number in both sets of multiples is 4, so that's the lowest common multiple. Write down the lowest common multiple of these numbers.

3 and 5 _____

4 and 6 _____

5 and 7 _____

Finished? Give yourself a gold star, then it's joke time.
Why did one fifth need to chill out?

Answer: Because he was too "tense!" (two-tenths)

Place value

Numbers are made up of one or more digits from 0 to 9. You can write any number using just these digits! This is because of place value. Each place in a number stands for a different amount. Look at the grid below.

Millions	Hundred thousands	Ten thousands	Thousands	Hundreds	Tens	Units

Find your place
A number could be 2, 20, 200, 2,000 or 20,000 or even 200,000! Where the digit sits tells us how much it's worth. For example, the 2 in 20 is worth 2 tens, while the 2 in 2,000 is worth 2 thousands. The 0 holds the place, so we know how big the number is. Fill in the gaps below.

A 2-digit number shows how many tens and _____.

Tens	Units
3	4

A 3-digit number shows how many _____, tens and units.

Hundreds	Tens	Units
8	3	9

You can go all the way up to a million (a 7-digit number) and beyond!

A 4-digit number shows how many _____, hundreds, _____ and units.

Thousands	Hundreds	Tens	Units
5	6	4	9

10

Finished? Give yourself a gold star.

Can you solve this riddle? How many times can you subtract 10 from 100?

Answer: Once (next time you'll take 10 from 90)

Complete the grid

Using these three numbers, complete the grid. Part of each number is filled in for you already.

5649   3833   9275

Thousands	Hundreds	Tens	Units
5			
	8		
		7	

Tip time!
To help you remember the place value columns, pick words that start with the same letters, such as: Tiger for Thousands, Hamster for Hundreds, Toad for Tens and Unicorn for Units.

For larger numbers you could use other words, such as Monkey for Millions.

Made up names are good for remembering too: Theo Thousands, Harry Hundreds, Terry Tens, Usain Units.

Number cards

Look at these 4 number cards.
What's the highest 3-digit number you can make?
What's the lowest 3-digit number you can make?

| 8 | 3 | 6 | 5 |

Highest: _____   Lowest: _____

Finished? Give yourself a gold star. Can you solve this riddle? If you multiply me by any number, the answer will always be the same. What am I?

Answer: Zero

11

Ordering and sequences

Once we know place value, we can easily order lists of numbers from highest to lowest or lowest to highest. Lists of numbers may also follow a pattern or sequence.

Ordering

Put these numbers in order, from the lowest number to the highest.

746   935   263   46   8

Now put these numbers in order, from the highest number to the lowest.

489   245   29   83   111

Sequences

A sequence means something that follows on from something else. Some of the easiest sequences are times tables.

Write down the next number in each sequence below. Think about how the units, tens or hundreds increase (or decrease) and by how much.

14   17   20   23

121   131   141

365   464   563

12

Finished? Give yourself a gold star, then it's joke time.
Are monsters good at maths?

Answer: Not unless you count Dracula!

Maths operations

There are four basic operations in maths. You may hear them referred to in different ways.

Symbol	Maths operation	Other words used
+	Addition	add, plus, sum, total
−	Subtraction	subtract, minus, take away
x	Multiplication	multiply, times, product
÷	Division	divide, share

Operation match

Draw a line between the sentence and the symbol that tells you what operation to do. Then write out the sum and calculate the answer. The first one has been done for you.

Tia and Adi have five apples each. How many apples do they have in total?	**x**	
Aaron has two yogurts in his lunchbox. Mum takes one away. How many does he have left?	**+**	5 + 5 = 10
Maya has thirty game cards. She decides to share them out equally among three friends. How much does each friend get?	**−**	
Freddie scores ten goals. Daniel scores five times as many goals as Freddie. How many goals does Daniel score?	**÷**	

Finished? Give yourself a gold star, then it's joke time.
Why are surgeons good at maths?

Answer: Because they know how to do operations!

Measuring and converting

You'll find measurements everywhere you look! We measure things to find their length, width, height, distance, weight and capacity (volume of liquid).

Units of measurement
There are standard measurements that everyone uses. We use different instruments to measure things. Tick the correct unit of measurement for each of these instruments.

	Centimetres ✓	Grams ☐	Kilometres ☐
	Metres ☐	Kilometres ☐	Litres ☐
	Litres ☐	Millimetres ☐	Grams ☐
	Metres ☐	Grams ☐	Centimetres ☐
	Kilometres ☐	Centilitres ☐	Kilograms ☐

We can convert between different units of measurements, such as kilometres to metres. There are 1,000 metres (m) in 1 kilometre (km). Convert these measurements into metres or kilometres.

1 km = _____ m
3,000 m = _____ km

5 km = _____ m
10,000 m = _____ km

14

Finished? Give yourself a gold star. Can you solve this riddle?
What weighs more: a kilo of potatoes or a kilo of feathers?

Answer: They weigh the same (a kilo).

Parcel mix-up!

Postwoman Patricia has got her parcels all muddled up. Read the clues and match up the parcel with its owner.

Ben's parcel is a circle shape. It's so light you can bounce it!

Aunty Tansy's parcel is twice as heavy as Ben's parcel.

Anna's sister sent her a present in a pretty box. It didn't weigh much at all.

Graham's parcel is heavy. He needs it for his garden.

110g

800g

22.5Kg

400g

Largest amounts

There are 1000 grams (g) in 1 kilogram (kg) and 1000 millilitres (ml) in 1 litre (l). Circle the largest amount in each box.

1kg 100g 300g	2l 3,000ml 200ml	300g 2Kg 3,500g	4l 2,400ml 4,200ml

Finished? Give yourself a gold star. Can you solve this riddle?
I'm as light as a feather, but even the strongest person can't hold me for long. What am I?

Answer: Breath.

Measuring temperature

If we want to measure how hot or cold something is, we use a thermometer. A thermometer is marked in degrees Celsius (°C). Have a go at these measuring challenges!

What's the temperature?

Colour in each thermometer so that it shows the temperature written underneath. The first one has been done for you.

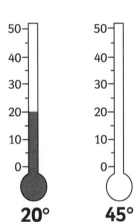

20°   **45°**   **22°**   **15°**   **2°**

Tip time!

The hotter the temperature, the higher the positive number (above 0°C). The colder it is, the higher the negative number (below 0°C).

World temperatures

Temperatures vary widely around the world, from over 50°C in Death Valley, USA, to −30°C in Antarctica! Look at this world map, which shows some average temperatures, and answer the questions.

What is the hottest place on the map?

_____

Name the coldest place.

_____

Which place is closest in temperature to the UK?

_____

Which place is closest in temperature to Bangkok, Thailand?

San Francisco, USA: 14°C

Moscow, Russia: 10°C

London, UK: 11°C

Antarctica: −10°C

Bangkok, Thailand: 30°C

Finished? Give yourself a gold star, then it's joke time.
Who's in charge of the pencil case?

Answer: The ruler!

Measuring time

Analogue clocks

An analogue clock has a face with the numbers marked 1 to 12. We use it to tell the time in 12-hour measurements. We call the morning a.m. and the afternoon p.m. Write the time each clock is showing. The first one has been done for you.

half past one   _____   _____   _____

Digital clocks

Digital clocks use only digits to tell us the time in 24-hour measurements. Using the chart to help you, draw the correct time on the clock faces to match the 24-hour clock time shown beneath each clock.

24	0:00	1:00	2:00	3:00	4:00	5:00	6:00	7:00	8:00	9:00	10:00	11:00
a.m.	12:00	1:00	2:00	3:00	4:00	5:00	6:00	7:00	8:00	9:00	10:00	11:00
24	12:00	13:00	14:00	15:00	16:00	17:00	18:00	19:00	20:00	21:00	22:00	23:00
p.m.	12:00	1:00	2:00	3:00	4:00	5:00	6:00	7:00	8:00	9:00	10:00	11:00

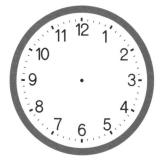  

21:00   *05:15*   *10.20*   *13:45*

Finished? Give yourself a gold star, then it's joke time.
How can you make time fly?

Answer: Throw the clock out the window!

2D Shapes

2D shapes are flat not fat! They have different names, depending on how many sides or edges they have. Look at the page you are reading. It has four sides. Two sides are longer than the other, which makes it a rectangle.

How many sides?
Count the sides of each shape and write the number in the middle.
The first one has been done for you.

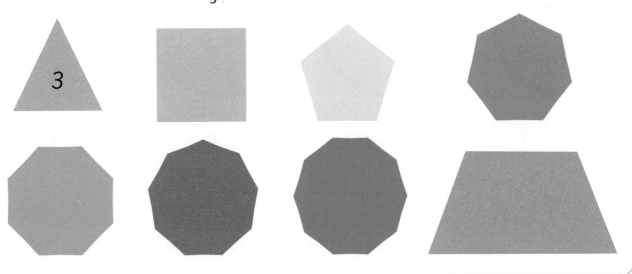

Who am I?
Draw a line to match up each statement below with the correct shape.
The first one has been done for you.

I have six sides.

I have seven sides.

I have three sides.

I have nine sides.

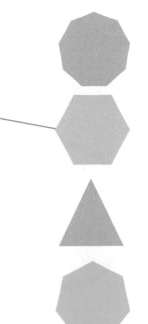

Finished? Give yourself a gold star, then it's joke time.
Why didn't anybody talk to the circle?

Answer: Because there was no point!

Shapes are everywhere!

Look at these everyday objects. Count how many of each shape you can see and write your answer in boxes below. A hexagon has six sides.

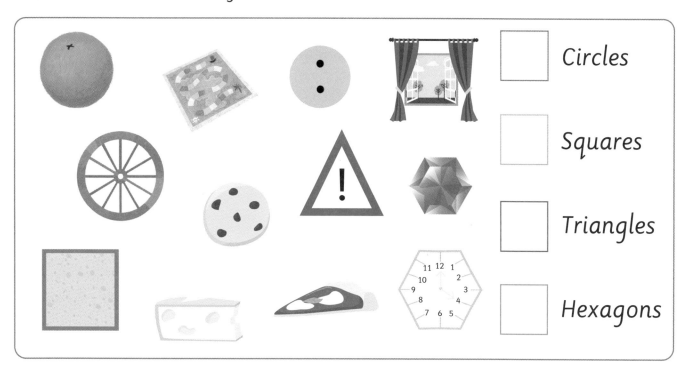

Circles

Squares

Triangles

Hexagons

Animal shapes

You can make animals using only 2D shapes.
Copy this owl into the box below. Use a ruler to help you.

Finished? Give yourself a gold star, then it's joke time.
What did the square say to the circle?

Answer: Haven't I seen you around?

3D Shapes

3D shapes are fat not flat! They are made out of regular 2D shapes and they also have extra surfaces called "faces". If you look at a dice, it has 6 square faces. This makes it a cube.

Name the shape

3D shapes get their names from how many edges and faces they have, also called their properties. Draw a line to match each shape to its name.

Cylinder   Sphere   Cuboid   Triangular prism

Cone   Square-based pyramid   Cube   Hexagonal prism

Riddle me!

Solve these riddles and write the answers in the spaces.

Roll me there and roll me here,
I have one face, I'm a _____ !

If you like ice cream, you're not alone!
Eat it from a cup or from a _____ .

I'm not a cone or ball or tube.
My faces are square, so I'm a _____ .

I point to the sky. The Egyptians did!
They made me into a _____ !

Finished? Give yourself a gold star, then it's joke time.
What do you get when you cross a pebble with a sphere?

Answer: Rock and roll!

Nets of 3D shapes

A net is what a 3D shape looks like, if it is opened out flat.
Colour the correct net for each 3D shape.

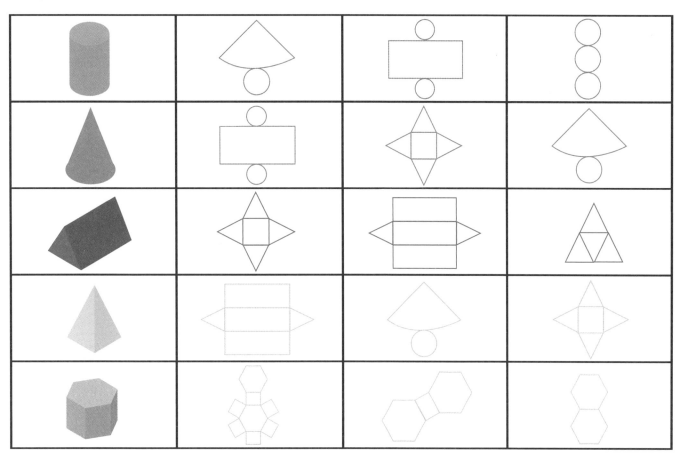

Faces and edges

Complete the table below to show the properties of each 3D shape.
Write down examples of everyday 3D objects.

	Faces	Edges	Example
Sphere	1		ball
Cone		1	
Cylinder			
Cube			
Cuboid			

Finished? Give yourself a gold star, then it's joke time.
How do you count cows?

Answer: With a cow-culator!

21

Graphs

A graph is used to display information that is connected in some way, such as change over time. On a graph we plot points that are joined with straight lines.

Making your mark

To mark points on a graph, draw two lines that cross in the middle. The line going across is the x axis. The line going up and down is the y axis. The centre point is 0. Using a ruler, have a go at drawing your own graph, using the example to help you.

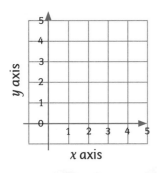

Practise drawing a line on this graph from where the two zeros meet to where the two tens meet.

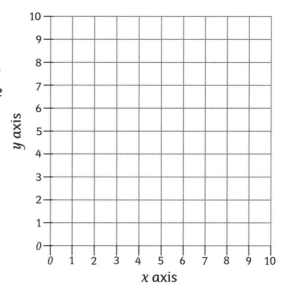

Tip time! **We use gridded paper to make a graph.**

Co-ordinates

Points on a grid have two numbers to help you work out their position, known as co-ordinates. Each point has an x axis number and a y axis number. Always start by going across the graph first, then up or down. Write down the co-ordinates for the points labelled A to D on the graph below. The first one has been done for you.

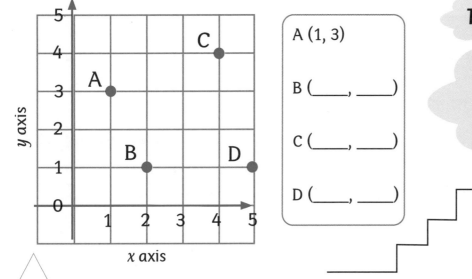

A (1, 3)

B (____, ____)

C (____, ____)

D (____, ____)

Tip time!

To help you remember which direction to plot co-ordinates, remember this riddle.

Go along the corridor and up the stairs!

Finished? Give yourself a gold star. Can you solve this riddle?
If you draw a line, how can you make it longer without touching it?

Answer: Draw a shorter line next to it, and the line will appear longer!

Pirate treasure!

Plot each of these coordinates onto the treasure map using a cross.
The first one has been done for you.

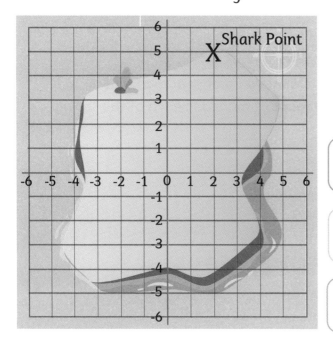

Tip time!

Line graphs can have both positive and negative numbers. These numbers become negative once they cross either axis.

Shark Point (2, 5)

Dead Man's Mountain (3, 2)

Skull Creek (-3 -2)

Parrot's Paradise (−1, 1)

Buried treasure (2, -2)

Picture plotting

Plot these co-ordinates on the graph. Join them up to reveal the mystery picture!
Colour it in when you've finished.

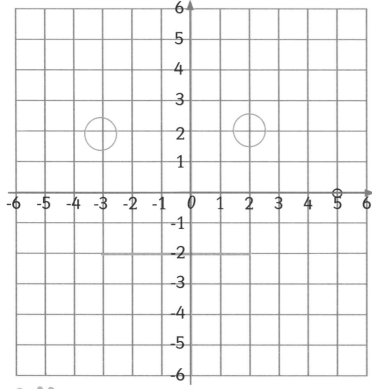

A (-4, 4)

B (3,-4)

C (-4, -3)

D (-3, -4)

E (-3, -6)

F (4, -3)

G (3, -6)

H (4, 4)

Finished? Give yourself a gold star. Can you solve this riddle?
What number can only go up?

Answer: Your age!

Money

Money is what we use to pay for something. Different countries have different types of money. This is called currency.

Pounds and pence

In the UK, we use a currency called pound sterling. It is made up of pence (p) and pounds (£). Count these coins and notes, then write the total amount of money in each of the spaces.

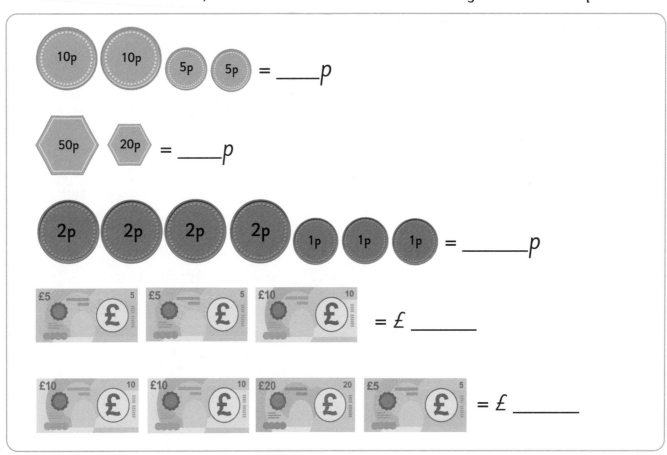

Decimal points

There are 100p in £1. When we write out amounts of money, we place a decimal point between the pounds and the pence.

£5 and 20p = £5.20   £20 and 2p = £20.02

Write these amounts out correctly, using a £ sign and decimal point.

564p   383p   982p   2075p   3724p   1p

_____   _____   _____   _____   _____   _____

Finished? Give yourself a gold star, then it's joke time.
Where do fish keep their money?

Answer: In a river bank!

Pet shop

Dylan has saved up £130 to buy a pet rabbit. He goes to the pet shop to get what he needs to look after his rabbit. Add up all the prices and write the total below.

Rabbit:	£25.00
Rabbit feed:	£13.50
Hutch:	£60.00
Water bottle:	£3.00
Hay:	£10.00
Feeding bowl:	£4.50

Total _____

Does Dylan have enough money to buy everything he needs?

Yes ☐   No ☐

Design your own banknote

If you could design a new banknote for people to use, what would it look like? What colour would it be? What pictures would you include? You could also decide on a new currency name, such as your surname or your pet's name. Draw your banknote here.

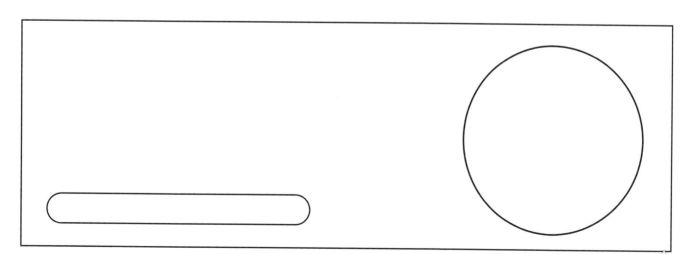

Finished? Give yourself a gold star, then it's joke time.
If two's company and three's a crowd, what are four and five?

Answer: 9

Lines of symmetry

When a shape has one half that exactly matches the other, we say it has a line of symmetry. Read these rules about symmetry and have a go at the challenges.

Shapes for symmetry

If you draw a line down the centre of a shape, you will have two pieces that are exactly the same. This butterfly has one line of symmetry. It is the same on both sides.

Tick the box below the shapes with the correct line of symmetry. Draw in the correct line of symmetry on those that are incorrect.

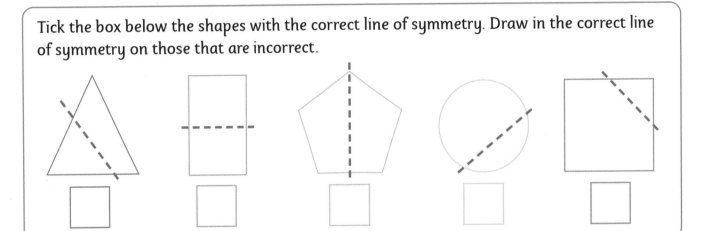

How many lines?

Some shapes have more than one line of symmetry. A square has four!
Draw lines of symmetry on these shapes. The number below each shape shows how many lines of symmetry it has. The first one has been done for you.

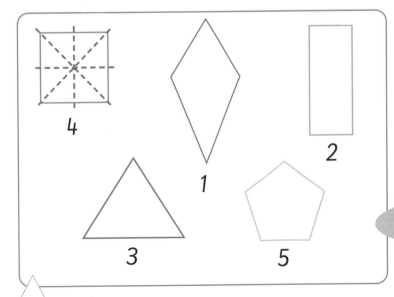

Tip time!

Cut out and fold shapes in half to find their lines of symmetry.

You'll be able to see clearly that one side is the same as the other.

26

Finished? Give yourself a gold star, then it's joke time.
Which season does a maths teacher like best?

Answer: SUMmer!

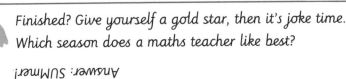

Roman numerals

Roman numerals are the numbers that were used in ancient Rome. You can still see them today, such as on the clock face of London's Big Ben.

What do they look like?
Roman numerals look like letters.
There are seven altogether.

I	V	X	L	C	D	M

You can combine the numerals to make other numbers. When a smaller number appears in front of a bigger one, it is subtracted. So IV is 4 (5 − 1) and IX is 9 (10 − 1). You can add numbers on, too. So XX is 20 (10 + 10). Using the chart to help you, write the correct Roman numerals next to each number.

1	I		9	IX
2	II		10	X
3	III		50	L
4	IV		60	LX
5	V		100	C
6	VI		500	D
7	VII		1000	M
8	VIII		2000	MM

4 = _____

10 = _____

30 = _____

55 = _____

93 = _____

All about me
Fill in this table using Roman numerals!

My age		My shoe size	
Number of people in my house		Birthday date	
Number of pets I have		Number of people in my class	

Finished? Give yourself a gold star, then it's joke time.
What do you call a number that likes to travel?

Answer: A "Roamin" numeral!

ROMAN NUMERALS

Mental maths

Working sums out in your head is an important skill! Test out what you've learned with these two mental maths challenges.

Challenge 1	Answer
Work out 15 + 7 + 2	
How many sides does a pentagon have?	
What is 5 x 9?	
Write down the number six hundred and thirty-three.	
Fill in the missing number: 20 ___ 32 38 44	
How do you write the number 9 in Roman numerals?	
What 3D shape has six faces?	
Simplify $\frac{3}{6}$	
An apple costs 36p. How much change will you get from 50p?	
Work out 164 – 73	
Total score =	

Finished? Give yourself a gold star. Can you solve this riddle?
The more you take away from me, the bigger I get. What am I?

Answer: A hole.

Challenge 2	Answer
Work out 16 − 4 − 3	
How many sides does an octagon have?	
What is 11 x 11?	
Simplify $\frac{4}{12}$	
How do you write 100 in Roman numerals?	
What is the value of 4 in the number 4758?	
Divide 63 by 9	
How many centimetres are there in a metre?	
What 3D shape is a can of drink?	
How many lines of symmetry does a rectangle have?	
Total score =	

Finished? Give yourself a gold star. Can you solve this riddle?
Three numbers give the same result when added together and multiplied together. What are they?

Answer: 1, 2 and 3

Challenge 3	Answer
Work out 22 − 2 − 4	
How many sides does a triangle have?	
What is 7 x 8?	
Simplify $\frac{4}{16}$	
How do you write 1000 in Roman numerals?	
What is the value of 7 in the number 2176?	
Divide 81 by 9	
How many millimetres are there in a centimetre?	
What 3D shape is an orange?	
A bike costs £97.00. How much change will you get from £100.00?	
Total score =	

Give yourself a gold star when you complete this page. There are lots of stars left over. Make yourself a reward chart to use them up!

Answers

P4 – 9 Times table: finding patterns
36, 54, 63, 90

P5 – 11 times table: double it up!

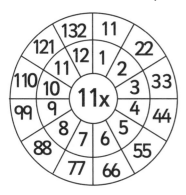

P6 – Divide it up
4, 4, $\frac{1}{4}$

P6 – How much pizza
$\frac{1}{5}$ $\frac{1}{12}$

P7 – Whole and parts

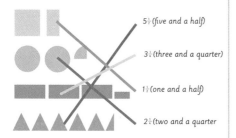

5½ (five and a half)
3¼ (three and a quarter)
1½ (one and a half)
2¼ (two and a quarter)

P7 – Naming fractions
$\frac{1}{3}$ $\frac{1}{4}$ $\frac{1}{2}$

P8 – Add these fractions
$\frac{1}{5} + \frac{2}{5} = \frac{3}{5}$ $\frac{2}{9} + \frac{5}{9} = \frac{7}{9}$ $\frac{2}{7} + \frac{3}{7} = \frac{5}{7}$

P8 – Simplify these fractions
$\frac{4}{12} = \frac{1}{3}$ $\frac{5}{15} = \frac{1}{3}$ $\frac{6}{18} = \frac{1}{3}$

P9 – Subtract these fractions
$\frac{7}{9} - \frac{5}{9} = \frac{2}{9}$ $\frac{3}{5} - \frac{2}{5} = \frac{1}{5}$ $\frac{7}{12} - \frac{5}{12} = \frac{2}{12}$

P10 – Lowest common multiple
$\frac{1}{2} - \frac{1}{4} = \frac{1}{4}$

P10 – Multiples
15, 12, 35

P10 – Find your place
units
hundreds
thousands / tens

P11 – Complete the grid
5649, 3833, 9275

Thousands	Hundreds	Tens	Units
5	6	4	9
3	8	3	3
9	2	7	5

P11 – Number cards
Highest: 8653
Lowest: 3568

P12 – Ordering
Lowest to highest: 8, 46, 263, 746, 935
Highest to lowest: 489, 245, 111, 83, 29

P12 – Sequences
14, 17, 20, 23, 26
121, 131, 141, 151
365, 464, 563, 662

P13 – Operation match

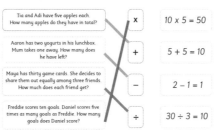

P14 – Units of measurement
Centimetres
Litres
Millimetres
Grams
Kilometres

1km = 1,000m   5km = 5,000m
3,000m = 3km   10,000m = 10km

P15 – Parcel mix up

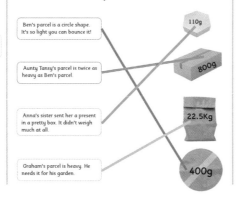

P15 – Largest amounts

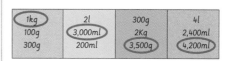

P16 – What's the temperature?

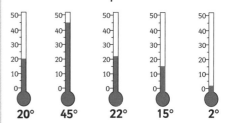

20°   45°   22°   15°   2°

P16 – World temperatures
What is the hottest place on the map?
Thailand
Name the coldest place.
Antarctica
Which place is closest in temperature
to London, UK?
Moscow, Russia
Which place is closest in temperature
to Bangkok, Thailand?
San Francisco, USA

P17 – Analogue clocks
half past one
quarter past two
quarter to seven
eleven o'clock

P17 – Digital clocks

21:00   05:15   10.20   13:45

P18 – 2D Shapes

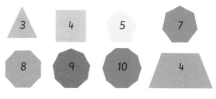

3   4   5   7
8   9   10   4

P18 – Who am I?

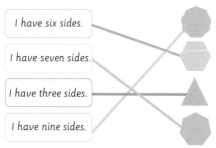

I have six sides.
I have seven sides.
I have three sides.
I have nine sides.

Answers

ANSWERS

P19 — Shapes are everywhere
Circles: 4
Squares: 3
Triangles: 3
Hexagons: 2

p20 — 3D Shapes

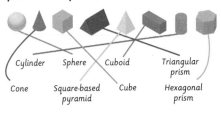

Cylinder Sphere Cuboid Triangular prism
Cone Square-based pyramid Cube Hexagonal prism

p20 — 3D Shapes

Roll me there and roll me here, I have one face, I'm a square!

If you like ice cream, you're not alone!
Eat it from a cup or from a cone!

I'm not a cone or ball or tube.
My faces are square, so I'm a cube!

I point to the sky. The Egyptians did!
They made me into a pyramid!

p21 — Nets of 3D shapes

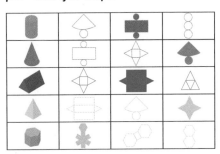

p21 — Faces and edges

	Faces	Edges	Example
Sphere	1	0	ball
Cone	2	1	ice cream
Cylinder	3	2	can of cola
Cube	6	12	dice
Cuboid	6	12	brick

p22 — Making your mark

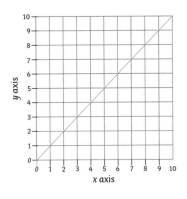

P22 — Co-ordinates
A 1, 3
B 2, 1
C 4, 4
D 5,1

p23 — Pirate treasure!

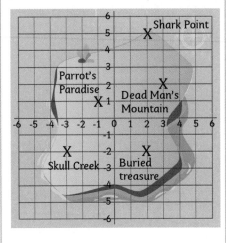

p23 — Picture plotting

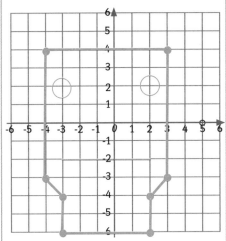

P24 — Pounds and pence
30p
70p
11p
£20
£45

p24 — Decimal points
£5.64
£3.83
£9.82
£20.75
£37.24
£0.01

P24 — Pounds and pence
30p
70p
11p
£20
£45

p24 — Decimal points
£5.64
£3.83
£9.82
£20.75
£37.24
£0.01

p25 — Pet shop
£116.00
Yes

p26 —Shapes for symmetry

p26 —How many lines?

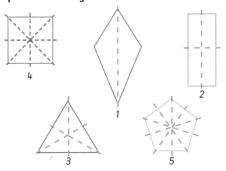

4   1   3   5   2

p27 — What do I look like?
4 = IV
10 = X
30 = X X X
55 = LV
93 = XCIII

p27 — Mental maths challenge 1
24, 5, 45, 633, 26, IX, cube or cuboid, ½, 14p, 91

p28 — Mental maths challenge 2
9, 8, 121, ⅓, C, four thousand, 7 , 100, cylinder, 2

p29 — Mental maths challenge 3
16, 3, 56, ¼, M, seventy, 9, 10, sphere, £3.00